Pop/Rock Songs of the Earth

Edited by JERRY L. WALKER

SCHOLASTIC BOOK SERVICES
New York Toronto London Auckland Sydney Tokyo

Photo credits—Scholastic photography awards: p. 4, Paul Margolies; pp. 6-7, Lawrence Brown; p. 8, Michael Hodges; p. 17, Marsha Stamp; pp. 18-19, Susan Emmich; p. 22, Douglas Wilkinson; p. 28, p. 96, John Engelman; p. 32, Mark Morris; p. 44, George Lee White; pp. 54-55, Kurt Smith; p. 66, Carter Ames; pp. 67-68, Richard Metcalf; p. 72, Paul Taylor; pp. 78-79, John Badley; p. 82, Robert Cergol; p. 88, Emily Wheeler; p. 94, John Christopher.

Additional photo credits: pp. 24, 26-27, 34, 59, Joseph J. Sia; p. 51, United Press International Photo; p. 50, Columbia Records; pp. 58, 62, KLN Photos, Inc.; pp. 74, 75, p. 86, J. Laurie.

 Published by Scholastic Book Services, a division of Scholastic Magazines, Inc.

1st printing . . . . March 1972

Printed in the U.S.A.

CONTENTS

INTRODUCTION

Modern songwriters and recording artists are doing an important new thing for us. They're not just writing and singing songs about love and happiness. Instead, they are asking us many important questions about survival. Can Earth be saved from destruction? Have we polluted its air and waters beyond the point of ever making them clean again? Have we destroyed so much plant and animal life that we have upset the balance of nature forever? Have we used up so many of Earth's natural resources that it can't continuc to support life as we know it much longer? Have we overpopulated to the point where the future holds certain starvation for millions of people? Has man lost his ability to care about others?

These are some of the questions raised by the lyrics in this book. Answers have to be found. We can't go on living as we have. Our ignorance, carelessness, laziness, and greed have certainly spoiled much of Earth. But maybe it isn't too late for us to improve things. Even if we can't correct all the ecological errors we've made, maybe we can at least keep things from getting worse.

The first step in our battle to save ourselves is to identify the problems, and that's what the lyrics in this book do. They are good songs and fun to listen to, but more important they can open our eyes to the problems around us. The 1971 United Fund drive had a good slogan, "If you don't do it, it won't get done." Read the lyrics, find out what some of the problems are, and then go out and *do* something about them.

THE BEATLES

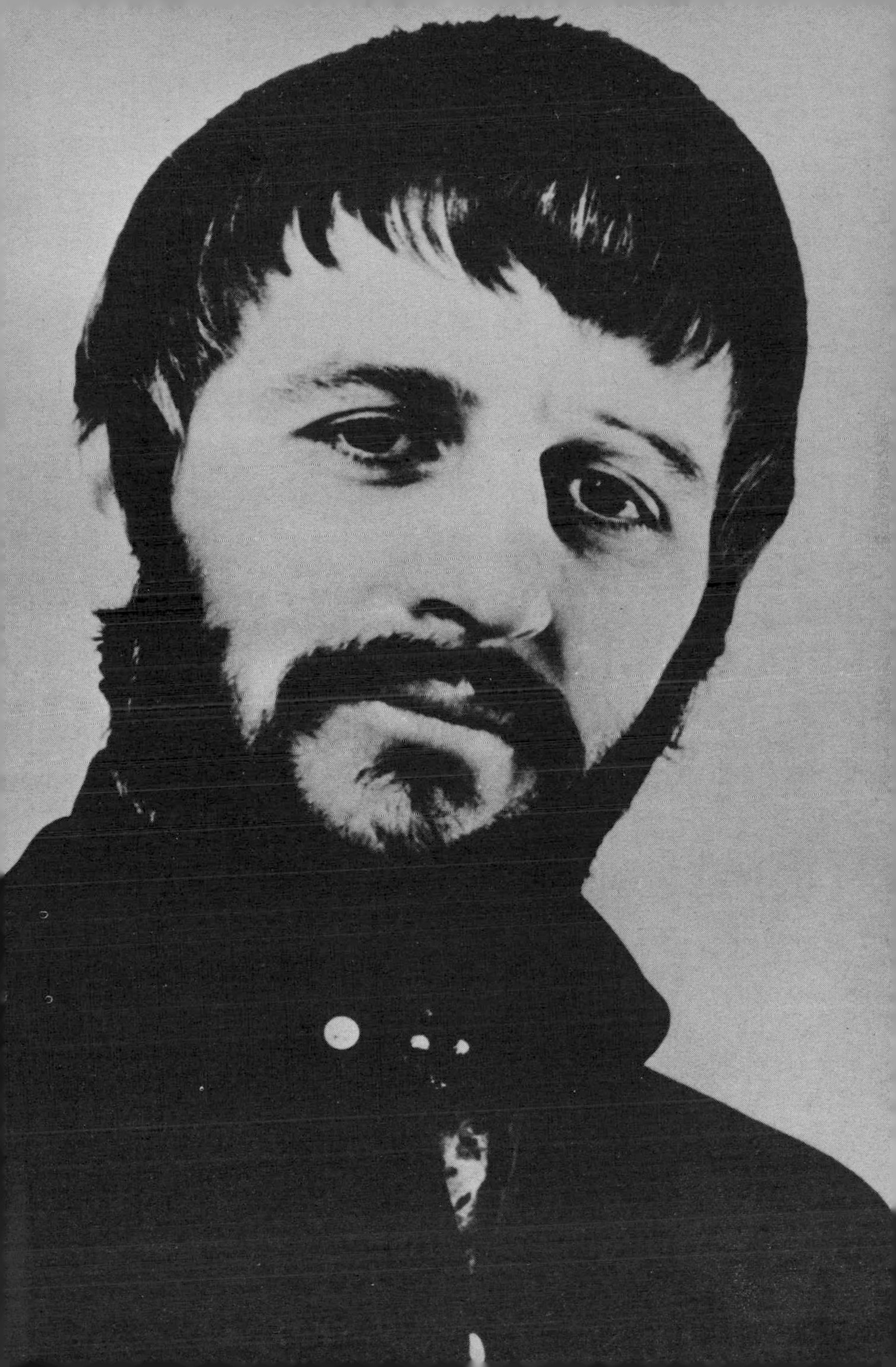

ACROSS THE UNIVERSE

John Lennon and Paul McCartney

Words are flying out like endless rain into a paper
cup,
They slither while they pass, they slip away across
the universe.
Pools of sorrow, waves of joy, are drifting through
my open mind, possessing and caressing me.
Jai Guru De Va Om.
Nothing's gonna change my world;
Nothing's gonna change my world.

Images of broken light which dance before me
like a million eyes,
That call me on and on across the universe.
Thoughts meander like a restless wind inside a
letter box; they tumble blindly as they make their
way across the universe.
Jai Guru De Va Om.
Nothing's gonna change my world;
Nothing's gonna change my world.

Sounds of laughter, shades of earth, are ringing through my open views, inciting and inviting me.
Limitless undying love which shines around me like a million suns;
It calls me on and on across the universe.
Jai Guru De Va Om.
Nothing's gonna change my world;
Nothing's gonna change my world.

AIN'T IT A SAD THING?

R. Dean Taylor

Big brown tin can lyin' in the black sand.
We used to lie there and watch the day.
Ah, now the leaves have all turned gray.
Down by the river where the river don't flow,
We can't go there no more;
Down by the river where the river don't flow,
The birds don't sing. Ain't it a sad thing?
The little child upon my knee
Holds a picture of a tree.
Tears in his eyes say where they all go.
The tears in mine say I really don't know.
Down by the river where the river don't flow,
We can't go there no more.
Down by the river where the river don't flow,
The birds don't sing. Ain't it a sad thing?
To listen to the wind goin' over the land,
Listen to the reasons that you don't understand.
Reach out and take my hand and we'll run run
run run.
Cities eatin' up the land;
Progress eatin' up the man;
The writing's in the slime on the sewer wall;
You better look, see, or we're all gonna fall.

THE 5TH DIMENSION

AIR

James Rado and Gerome Ragni

Welcome, sulphur dioxide.
Hello, carbon monoxide.
The air, the air is ev'rywhere.
Breathe deep while you sleep, breathe deep.

Bless you, alcohol blood-stream.
Save me, nicotine lung steam.
Incense, incense is in the air.
Breathe deep while you sleep, breathe deep.

Cataclysmic ectoplasm,
Fallout atomic spasm
Vapor and fume at the stone of my tomb;
Breathing like a sullen perfume,
Eating at the stone of my tomb.

Welcome, sulphur dioxide.
Hello, carbon monoxide.
The air, the air is everywhere.
Breathe deep while you sleep, breathe deep!

PETE SEEGER

BELLS OF RHYMNEY

Idris Davies and Pete Seeger

"Oh, what will you give me?" say the sad bells
of Rhymney.
"Is there hope for the future?" cry the brown bells
of Merthyr.
"Who made the mine owner?" say the black bells
of Rhondda.
"And who robbed the miner?" cry the grim bells of
Blaina.

"They will plunder willy-nilly," cry the bells of
Caerphilly.
"They have fangs, they have teeth," shout the loud
bells of Neath.
"Even God is uneasy," say the moist bells of Swansea.
"And what will you give me?" say the sad bells
of Rhymney.

"Throw the vandals in court," say the bells of
Newport.
"All would be well if, if, if, if," cry the green bells
of Cardiff.
"Why so worried, sisters, why?" sang the silver
bells of Wye.
"And what will you give me?" say the sad bells
of Rhymney.

THE BEACH BOYS

COUNTRY AIR

Mike Love and Brian Wilson

Umh — uhumh! Umh — uhumh!

Get a breath of that country air.
Breathe the beauty of it ev'rywhere.

Umh — uhumh! Umh — uhumh!

Get a look at the clear blue sky.
Mother Nature fills my eye.

Umh — uhumh! Umh — uhumh!

Rise up early;
The day won't let you sleep.

Umh — uhumh! Umh — uhumh!

JAMES TAYLOR

Teaching Guide

POP/ROCK SONGS OF THE EARTH

by Jerry L. Walker

POP/ROCK SONGS OF THE EARTH is different from its predecessors in that all the lyrics included deal with issues related to ecology. Heretofore, our concern was to present good, recent lyrics by popular artists which could be used as lead-ins to poetry or as stimulants for interesting discussions and activities. That concern is built into this book too, but it has a greater concern, that of intensifying students' awareness of the ecological mess we have created. If that is accomplished, perhaps a commitment to do something about it will follow. None of us can afford to be apathetic about the issues raised in these lyrics, but especially the younger generation, for it is their future more than ours that is at stake.

For years the controversy has raged about the parameters

more fixed, more secure. Today when the existence of the entire human race is in jeopardy, it no longer makes much sense to quibble about whether a particular piece of material or a particular activity properly belongs to this or that subject-matter area. There are some issues of such overwhelming concern that they should be treated whenever and wherever the opportunity occurs. Ecology is such an issue, and the lyrics in this book can provide the opportunity to deal with it in any classroom.

General Teaching Suggestions

One way to work with these lyrics would be to make them the heart of a unit on the condition of the world today. Some of the lyrics, such as "Chelsea Morning," "Child of Mine," and "Country Road," present a picture of the world as we would like it to be, while nearly all the others describe the world as it is. The unit could begin with the students writing or talking about what they really want the world to be like. Following that, they could compare their ideal worlds with those described in the lyrics. Then they could try to identify the conditions that run counter to their ideal world and discuss which conditions can be changed and which cannot. The lyrics can certainly be used to help enumerate the problems, but they will, of course, have to be supplemented with materials from other media. The unit could conclude with the establishment of a set of resolutions or guidelines for action that must be followed if the ideal world is ever to be achieved.

The lyrics can also be the basis for a unit called "A Portrait

profile or portrait of mankind. An interesting activity would be to compare the portrait the lyrics provide with those provided by other media. Using one daily newspaper as their source, the students could study all the contents, including the news stories, features, advertisements, and comics, to see what kind of picture of mankind it provides. Pooling their experiences with radio, TV, and motion pictures, they could draw other portraits. Deciding which medium paints the most complete or accurate picture of what we are really like might be the culminating activity.

Another way to use these lyrics would be to plan a unit called "Questions and Answers." In this unit, each lyric would be studied for the major questions it raises about ecology, and the students could debate, discuss, and investigate the best answers to those questions. It would be useful to have the students decide which of their answers they could act upon right now and then let them set about doing it. Active involvement in the solution to some problem should be the goal, and certainly much learning would occur as the students identified the questions, posed answers, and planned strategies for action.

There are, of course, many other units that could be planned around these lyrics. The decision as to which would be most appropriate for a given class must be based at least in part upon the sophistication, interests, and abilities of the students. With any class, however, these lyrics can be used to create a greater awareness of the ecological problems that confront us and to get the students actively involved in the solutions to those problems. The fact that many of the lyrics are from popular songs of the recent past should help to provide motivation. Many of the students may not be interested in ecology, but most of them *are* interested in the music of their generation.

Providing the music to accompany these lyrics should create

you or the students can find recordings of the other songs. Hearing the songs is important because it provides the necessary overview for taking a closer look at the lyrics.

Suggestions for Teaching Individual Lyrics

Following are some suggestions for questions you might ask your students and for activities that might be used in conjunction with the lyrics.

ACROSS THE UNIVERSE

1. This seems to be someone who is opening his mind in meditation. What do you think the words "Jai Guru De Va Om" mean?
2. Would you be happy if nothing could change your world?
3. The rockets and satellites we keep sending out into the universe could be thought of as a kind of pollution. Do you think the time will come when that will be a problem?

AIN'T IT A SAD THING?

1. We usually think of progress as being a good thing. As Americans, we tend to think that what's new is good. Yet

2. Is it really possible, as the lyric suggests, that unless we stop pollution we may all be destroyed?
3. Write an essay about what the world would be like without something which we all take for granted, like fresh water, clean air, trees, or birds.
4. Suppose you asked your parents why they have let pollution get so bad. What do you think they would say? Ask several adults to see if you get different answers from different people.

AIR

1. Suppose you were a politician running for some high office, and the owners of some big factory offered you money to help pay for your campaign if you would fight against laws requiring them to install expensive antipollution devices in their factory. What would you do? Would you take their money?
2. What do you make of the tone of this lyric? Are the writers being serious when they say, "Welcome, sulphur dioxide. Hello, carbon monoxide"?
3. If we really wanted to clean up the air, what are some of the things we would have to do? What could you, personally, do?

BELLS OF RHYMNEY

miners. Can you think of any other groups of people who often take advantage of other groups? Why do you suppose they do it?

2. How would you complete the statement, "All would be well if..."?
3. Do you think there's hope for the future? Think about that question and then write either an essay or a short story describing what you think the future will be like.

CHELSEA MORNING

1. What does the line, "And we'll talk in present tenses" mean? What do you prefer to think about—yesterday, today, or tomorrow?
2. Look outside through some nearby window. What do you see that is either beautiful or ugly? Do you think others would agree with what you called beautiful or ugly?
3. Make a collage that would represent your "portrait of today." Use whatever pictures or objects you can find that show just what you really think about living conditions today.
4. Write your own description of what morning is like in your community. How different is it from a Chelsea morning?

CHILD OF MINE

1. This lyric has the lines, "The times you were born in may

which to be living? What makes it either good or bad? Do you think your generation will make the world a better place to live in than it has been? What will they do that will be different?

2. Do your parents see the world different from you? How much have your parents influenced the way you see things?
3. Does anyone have the right to tell someone else how to live his life? What about criminals? Do we have the right to put them in prison? What about people who pollute the atmosphere? Do we have the right to make them stop it?

COUNTRY AIR

1. How would you picture Mother Nature? Draw a picture or find a picture that represents your idea of Mother Nature.
2. What things do you associate with the country? Are they all good things? If you had a choice, would you rather live in the city or the country? What are the reasons for your choice?

COUNTRY ROAD

1. Do you think it's harder to be free in a city than in the country? Maybe it's just that different places offer different kinds of freedom. What do you think?
2. Make your own list of things a "natural-born fool" would do.
3. Do you think the person who is speaking in this lyric really knows where he wants the country road to take him?
4. Do you think it's a cop-out just to get up and walk away from the problems you face? Is it better for the person who thinks

life in the city is terrible to move to the country or should he stay in the city and try to make things better?

DON'T LOOK NOW

1. Try to answer the questions that this lyric asks. See if your friends would answer them differently. How do you account for the differences?
2. Make your own list of questions about the world that you would like to have answered.
3. The slogan for the 1971 United Fund Drive was "If you don't do it, it won't get done." Do you agree that if you want something done, you have to do it yourself? Are there some things you have to rely on others for? What are those things?
4. Do we have any responsibility for the people in the world who are starving? Will there always be starving people in the world?

FOR WHAT IT'S WORTH

1. If you had the power to get people to stop doing certain things, what would you tell them to stop doing?
2. Many people believe that the overcrowded conditions of the city are responsible for most of the violence that occurs there. Do you agree with that?
3. Write a theme on the topic, "The Best Way To Get People To Work Together."
4. Find a picture of what you think the person who is speak-

ing in this lyric would look like. Why did you choose the picture you did?

A HARD RAIN'S A-GONNA FALL

1. It may be that Bob Dylan is not really talking about the rain we know at all. Think of words you could substitute for the word "rain" every time it appears in the song.
2. Make a list of the worst things you have either seen or heard of and then after examining your list, see if it tells you anything about yourself that you didn't realize before. It may be that you will discover that it's always a certain kind of thing that you find terrible. If you compare your list with your friends' lists, you may find that they named entirely different kinds of things. If that is true, how do you account for the differences?
3. If all you had to judge the world by was this lyric, what kind of impression would you have? Do you think Dylan is exaggerating the situation?

HAVE YOU EVER SEEN THE RAIN?

1. This is another one of those lyrics that seem to say that you can't judge tomorrow by what it's like today. Even though it's sunny today, it may be storming tomorrow and, in fact, the sunny day may be one of the things that causes the storm. Can you think of any things that seem to be fine today that might lead to trouble in the future? What are they?
2. How many ways can you think of that the rain benefits us? Are there any ways that it hurts us?

HERE WE ARE IN THE YEARS

1. One of the lines in this lyric states that one condition of modern life is that lives become careers, which means that people just live to do their jobs. An interesting survey to conduct is to ask people to list what they are and then see how many people put what they do as workers before such things as "woman," "mother," and "human being."
2. Does it seem important to you that people have a chance to get away from the city once in a while to relax and enjoy nature?
3. Write a theme on the topic, "Where I Would Like To Go To Really Relax."
4. Do you think that life on Earth will ever get so crowded and difficult that people will have to live on other planets if they want to live quiet, peaceful lives?

I DON'T EAT ANIMALS

1. Is this lyric a good argument for being a vegetarian? How do you suppose the writer can justify eating plants which are also living things?
2. A great many people today are concerned about the chemicals that are used to grow and prepare food. Examine the labels on such things as canned foods and bakery products to see if you can identify the chemicals that have been added as flavor enhancers or preservatives.
3. If you had to write a poem or lyric using the same first line as the one in this lyric ("I was just thinkin' 'bout the way it's s'posed to be"), what things would you write about?

THE LAMENT OF THE CHEROKEE RESERVATION INDIAN

1. Have you seen any movies or TV shows involving fights between Indians and white men where the Indians won the battle? How are Indians usually pictured in the westerns?
2. What would a red man be like deep inside? Do you suppose it's much different from being a white or black man?
3. The lyric mentions many things that were taken away from the Cherokees. Which of those things do you think the Indians resented most?

ME AND YOU AND A DOG NAMED BOO

1. What do you think it would be like just traveling around the country all the time? Write an essay about why you would or would not like to do that.
2. Make a list of all the sights you would like to see if you could travel any place you wanted to.
3. What kind of person would you like to travel across the land with? Write a description of that person.

MERCY MERCY ME

1. What things are you aware of that aren't what they used to be?
2. Do you think we will ever stop polluting the Earth's air and water? Do you think passing more laws will help?
3. Write a paper about what you as a single individual could do to fight pollution.

NOW THAT THE BUFFALO'S GONE

1. Having their own land was, and still is, very important to the Indians. Why is it so important to them?
2. What things should we do to help the Indians?
3. There are other animals besides the buffalo that are in danger of becoming extinct. Write what you think would be a good law to protect those animals and to keep others from becoming extinct.

POLLUTION

1. This lyric deals humorously with the problems caused by pollution. Which do you think would have more effect on the way people behave, a humorous lyric like this, or a more serious lyric like "Mercy Mercy Me"?
2. Do you think things are really as bad as this lyric suggests, or are the problems exaggerated in it? Write your own exaggerated picture of our pollution problems.
3. Make a collage using pictures and different objects to represent the pollution you'd find in some big city.

SO THE SEEDS ARE GROWING

1. Whom is the speaker in this lyric talking to? Whom should he be talking to?
2. How much freedom does any of us really have? How much freedom should each of us have?
3. Describe an experience you've had when it was true that there were too many voices and not enough ears.

TURN BACK, O MAN

1. Make a list of what you consider to be man's most foolish ways.
2. Do you think people two hundred years from now will still be doing the same bad things we're doing now?

WALKING THROUGH THE COUNTRY

1. Does your mood change with the weather? Many people seem to be happier on sunny days than they are on rainy days. Is that true of you? If it is, imagine what you'll feel like if pollution gets so bad that it constantly blocks out the sunshine.
2. Write a description of how it feels to your feet to walk barefoot through the grass.
3. What is the grooviest day you can remember? What happened to make it so groovy for you?

WHAT HAVE THEY DONE TO THE RAIN?

1. This is the third lyric in this book with the word "rain" in the title, but in every lyric it stands for something different from just the wet stuff that falls from the sky. Examine these lyrics to see if you can discover what it is that rain stands for in each one.
2. Many people love to walk in the rain. Do you? Write what it feels like to walk in the rain.

WHERE DO THE CHILDREN PLAY?

1. Write your own answer to the question that the title of this lyric asks. Where do the children in your neighborhood play? Is it a good place to play?
2. Do you think we will ever reach the point where there really will be so many buildings and roads that there will be no empty space left for parks and recreation areas?

WHERE HAVE ALL THE FLOWERS GONE?

1. What do you think is the most important thing a person could ever learn about life? Ask a number of people that question and compare the answers you get with your own. Are they different? Why?
2. Do you think we will ever stop having wars? What are the reasons for the answer you give?
3. Asking where all the flowers have gone is like asking where all the beauty has gone. What do you consider to be the most beautiful things in the world?

COUNTRY ROAD

James Taylor

Take to the highway;
Won't you lend me your name?
Your way and my way seem to be one and the same.
Mama don't understand it, she wants to know where
I've been.
I'd have to be some kind of natural-born fool to
want to pass that way again.
But you know, I could feel it on a country road.

Sail on home to Jesus, won't you, good girls and boys.
I'm all in pieces; you can have your own choice.
But I can see a heavenly band full of angels
Coming to set me free.
I don't know nothing 'bout the why or when,
But I can tell you that it's bound to be because I
could feel it on a country road.

I guess my feet know where they want me to go
Walking on a country road.
Walk on down, walk on down, walk on down,
walk on down, walking on a country road.
La la la la la la la la la la la la la la la la.
Country road, country road, country road.

JONI MITCHELL

CHELSEA MORNING

Joni Mitchell

Woke up, it was a Chelsea morning, and the first
  thing that I heard
Was a song outside my window, and the traffic
  wrote the words;
It came ringing up like Christmas bells, and rapping
  up like pipes and drums.

Oh, won't you stay?
We'll put on the day
And we'll wear it 'til the night comes.

Woke up, it was a Chelsea morning, and the first
  thing that I saw
Was the sun through yellow curtains, and a rainbow
  on the wall:
Blue, red, green, and gold to welcome you, crimson
  crystal beads to beckon.

Oh, won't you stay?
We'll put on the day;
There's a sun show every second.

Now the curtain opens on a portrait of today.
And the streets are paved with passersby.
And pigeons fly,
And papers lie,
Waiting to blow away.

Woke up, it was a Chelsea morning, and the first
thing that I knew
There was milk and toast and honey and a bowl
of oranges, too;
And the sun poured in like butterscotch and stuck
to all my senses.

Oh, won't you stay?
We'll put on the day
And we'll talk in present tenses.

When thc curtain closes and the rainbow runs away,
I will bring you incensc owls by night,
By candlelight,
By jewel-light,
If only you will stay.
Pretty baby, won't you?
Wake up? It is a Chelsea morning.

CAROLE KING

CHILD OF MINE

Gerry Goffin and Carole King

Although you see the world diff'rent from me,
Sometimes I can touch upon the wonders that
you see.
All the new colors and pictures you've designed,
Oh, yes, sweet darling, so glad you are a child of mine.
Child of mine, child of mine,
Oh, yes, sweet darling, so glad you are a child of mine.

You don't need direction; you know which way to go
And I don't want to hold you back; I just want to
watch you grow.
You're the one who taught me you don't have to
look behind.
Nobody's gonna kill your dreams or tell you how
to live your life,
There'll always be people to make it hard for a while
But you'll change their heads when they see you smile.

The times you were born in may not have been
the best,
But you can make the times to come better than
the rest.
I know you will be honest if you can't always be kind.
Oh, yes, sweet darling, so glad you are a child of mine.
Child of mine, child of mine,
Oh, yes, sweet darling, so glad you are a child of mine.

CREEDENCE CLEARWATER REVIVAL

DON'T LOOK NOW

J. C. Fogerty

Who'll take the coal from the mine?
Who'll take the salt from the earth?
Who'll take a leaf and grow it to a tree?
Don't look now, it ain't you or me.

Who'll work the field with his hands?
Who'll put his back to the plough?
Who'll take a mountain and give it to the sea?
Don't look now, it ain't you or me.

Don't look now, someone's done your starvin';
Don't look now, someone's done your prayin', too.

Who'll make the shoes for your feet?
Who'll make the cloak that you wear?
Who'll take a promise that you don't have to keep?
Don't look now, it ain't you or me.

Don't look now, someone's done your starvin';
Don't look now, someone's done your prayin', too.

Who'll take the coal from the mine?
Who'll take the salt from the earth?
Who'll take a promise that you don't have to keep?
Don't look now, it ain't you or me.

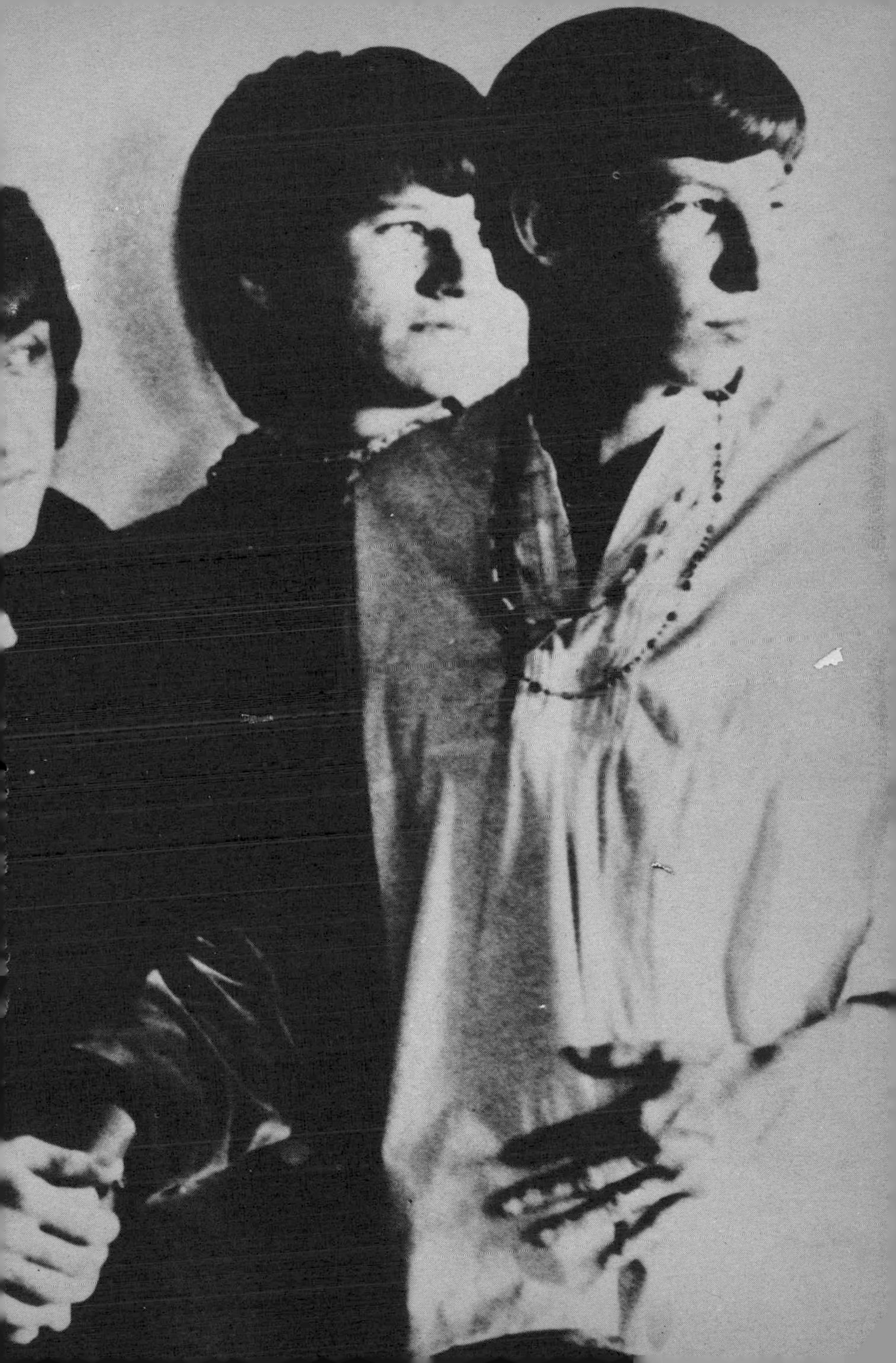

FOR WHAT IT'S WORTH

Stephen Stills

There's something happenin' here.
What it is ain't exactly clear.
There's a man with a gun over there,
Tellin' me I've got to beware.
It's time we stop, children.
What's that sound?
Everybody look what's goin' down.

There's battle lines bein' drawn.
Nobody's right if everybody's wrong.
Young people speakin' their minds,
Gettin' so much resistance from behind.
It's time we stop, children.
What's that sound?
Everybody look what's goin' down.

What a field day for the heat.
A thousand people in the street,
Singin' songs and carryin' signs
Mostly saying, "Hooray for our side."
It's time we stop, children.
What's that sound?
Everybody look what's goin' down.

Paranoia strikes deep;
Into your life it will creep
It starts when you're always afraid.
Step out of line, the Man come
And take you away.
You better stop, hey,
What's that sound?
Everybody look what's goin' down.

BOB DYLAN

A HARD RAIN'S A-GONNA FALL

Bob Dylan

Oh, where have you been, my blue-eyed son?
Oh, where have you been, my darling young one?
I've stumbled on the side of twelve misty mountains,
I've walked and I've crawled on six crooked highways,
I've stepped in the middle of seven sad forests,
I've been out in front of a dozen dead oceans,

I've been ten thousand miles in the mouth of a
graveyard,
And it's a hard, and it's a hard, it's a hard, and
it's a hard,
And it's a hard rain's a-gonna fall.

And what did you hear, my blue-eyed son?
And what did you hear, my darling one?

I heard the sound of a thunder, it roared out a warnin',
Heard the roar of a wave that could drown the whole
world,
Heard one hundred drummers whose hands were a
a-blazin',
Heard ten thousand whisperin' and nobody listenin',
Heard one person starve, I heard many people
laughin',
Heard the song of a poet who died in the gutter,
Heard the sound of a clown who cried in the alley,
And it's a hard, and it's a hard, it's a hard, it's a hard
And it's a hard rain's a-gonna fall.

Oh, what'll you do now, my blue-eyed son?
Oh, what'll you do now, my darling young one?

I'm a-goin' back out 'fore the rain starts a fallin',
I'll walk to the depth of the deepest black forest,
Where the people are many and their hands are all empty,
Where the pellets of poison are flooding their waters,
Where the home in the valley meets the damp dirty prison,
Where the executioner's face is always well hidden,
Where hunger is ugly, where souls are forgotten,
Where black is the color, where none is the number,
And I'll tell it and think it and breathe it,
And reflect it from the mountain so all souls can see it,
Then I'll stand on the ocean until I start sinkin',

But I'll know my song well before I start singin',
And it's a hard, it's a hard, it's a hard, it's a hard,
It's a hard rain's a-gonna fall.

HAVE YOU EVER SEEN THE RAIN?

J. C. Fogerty

Someone told me long ago,
There's a calm before the storm.
I know,
And it's been comin' for some time.

I want to know,
Have you ever seen the rain?
I want to know,
Have you ever seen the rain
Comin' down a sunny day?

When it's over, so they say,
It'll rain a sunny day.
I know,
Shinin' down like water.

I want to know,
Have you ever seen the rain?
I want to know,
Have you ever seen the rain
Comin' down a sunny day?

Yesterday and days before
Sun is cold and rain is hard.
I know,
Been that way for all my time.

I want to know,
Have you ever seen the rain?
I want to know,
Have you ever seen the rain
Comin' down a sunny day?

'Til forever on it goes
Through the circle, fast and slow.
I know,
And it can't stop, I wonder.

I want to know,
Have you ever seen the rain?
I want to know,
Have you ever seen the rain
Comin' down a sunny day?

NEIL YOUNG

HERE WE ARE IN THE YEARS

Neil Young

Now that the holidays have come,
They can relax and watch the sun
Rise above all of the beautiful things they've done:
Go to the country, take the dog,
Look at the sky without the smog,
See the world, laugh at the farmers feeding hogs,
Eat hot dogs.

What a pity
That the people from the city
Can't relate to the slower things
That the country brings.

Time itself is bought and sold.
The spreading fear of growing old
Contains a thousand games that we play.
While people planning trips to stars
Allow another boulevard
To claim a quiet country lane.
It's insane.
So the subtle face is a loser this time around.

Here we are in the years
Where the showman shifts the gears.
Lives become careers.
Children cry in fear,
"Let us out of here."

MELANIE

I DON'T EAT ANIMALS (AND THEY DON'T EAT ME)

Melanie Safka

I was just thinkin' 'bout the way it's s'posed to be:
I'll eat the plants and the growths 'round the trees.
And I'll live on veg'tables, and I'll grow on seeds,
And I won't eat animals, and they won't eat me.
Oh no, I don't eat animals 'cause I love 'em, you see.
Oh, I don't eat animals, I want nothin' dead in me.

I live on life so my life will live on me.
You know, I'll become life, so that life will become
me.

I don't eat white flour, white sugar makes you rot.
Oh, white could be beautiful, but mostly it's not.
A little bit of whole meal, some raisins and cheese,
But I don't eat animals, and they don't eat me.
Oh no, I don't eat animals 'cause I love 'em, you see.
Oh, I don't eat animals, I want nothin' dead in me.

I live on life so my life will live on me.
You know, I'll become life, so that life will become
me.

I don't eat the plants and the fruit from the trees,
And I live on veg'tables, and I grow on seeds.
A little bit of whole meal, some raisins and cheese,
But I don't eat animals, I want nothin' dead in me.
You know, I don't eat animals, I want nothin' dead in me.

I live on life so my life will live on me.
You know, I'll become life, so that life will become me.

THE LAMENT OF THE CHEROKEE RESERVATION INDIAN

John D. Loudermilk

They took the whole Cherokee nation
And put us on this reservation.
They took away our way of life,
The tomahawk, the bow and knife.
They put our papoose in a crib,
And took the buckskin from our rib.
They took away our native tongue,
And talk their English to our young.
The old teepee we all love so,
They're using now for just a show.
And all our beads we made by hand
Are nowadays made in Japan.
Although they've changed our ways of old,
They'll never change our hearts and souls.
Though I wear a man's shirt and tie,
I'm still a red man deep inside.
Hi ya yoh, hi ya yoh ho;
Hi ya yoh hi, hi ya yoh ho;
Hi ya yoh, hi ya yoh;
Hi ya yoh, hi ya yoh.
Oom ni ni ya, oom hi ya;
Oom hi ya oh, hi ya yoh, hi ya yoh.
Yip yip hi ya yoh, hi ya yoh hi.

ME AND YOU AND A DOG NAMED BOO

Kent LaVoie

I remember to this day
The bright red Georgia clay;
How it stuck to the tires after the summer rain.
Willpower made that old car go;
A woman's mind told me that it's so.
Oh, how I wish we were back on the road again,
Me and you and a dog named Boo.
Travelin' and livin' off the land,
Me and you and a dog named Boo.
How I love bein' a free man.

I can still recall the wheat fields of Saint Paul,
And the mornin' we got caught robbin' from an old
  hen.
Old MacDonald, he made us work
But then he paid us for what it was worth:
Another tank of gas and back on the road again,
Me and you and a dog named Boo.
Travelin' and livin' off the land,
Me and you and a dog named Boo.
How I love bein' a free man.

I'll never forget that day
We motored stately into big L.A.
The lights of the city put settlin' down in my brain.
Though it's been a month or so,
That old car's buggin' to go.
You gotta get away and get back on the road again,
Me and you and a dog named Boo.
Travelin' and livin' off the land,
Me and you and a dog named Boo.
How I love bein' a free man.

MERCY MERCY ME

Marvin Gaye

Oo oo ah, mercy mercy me,
Ah, things ain't what they used to be, no no.
Where did all the blue skies go?
Poison is the wind that blows from the north and
south and east.

Oo, mercy mercy me,
Mercy, father.
Ah, things ain't what they used to be, no no.
Oil wasted on the ocean and up on our sea;
Fish full of mercury.

Ah oh, mercy mercy me,
Ah, things ain't what they used to be, no no no.
Radiation underground and in the sky;
Animals and birds who live nearby are dying.

Oh, mercy mercy me,
Ah, things ain't the way they used to be.
What about this overcrowded land?
How much more abuse from man can she stand?
Oh na na, my sweet Lord,
No no, na na na,
My, my Lord, my sweet Lord.

BUFFY SAINTE-MARIE

NOW THAT THE BUFFALO'S GONE

Buffy Sainte-Marie

Can you remember the times
That you have held your head high
And told all your friends of your Indian claims,
Proud good lady, and proud good man?
Your great-great grandfather from Indian blood
sprang
And you feel in your heart for these ones.

Oh, it's written in books and in songs
That we've been mistreated and wronged.
Well, over and over I hear the same words
From you, good lady, from you, good man.
Well listen to me, if you care where we stand,
And you feel you're a part of these ones.

When a war between nations is lost,
The loser we know pays the cost.
But even when Germany fell to your hands,
Consider, dear lady, consider, dear man,
You left them their pride and left them their land.
And what have you done to these ones?

Has a change come about Uncle Sam,
Or are you still taking our land?
A treaty forever George Washington signed.
He did, dear lady, he did, dear man,
And the treaty's being broken by Kinzua Dam.
And what will you do for these ones?

Oh, it's all in the past you can say,
But it's still going on till today.
The government now wants the Iroquois land,
That of the Seneca and the Cheyenne.
It's here and it's now you must help us, dear man,
Now that the buffalo's gone.

POLLUTION

Tom Lehrer

If you visit American city,
You will find it very pretty.
Just two things of which you must beware:
Don't drink the water and don't breathe the air.

Pollution, pollution.
They've got smog and sewage and mud.
Turn on your tap and get
Hot- and cold-running crud.

See the halibuts and sturgeons
Being wiped out by detergents.
Fish gotta swim and birds gotta fly,
But they don't last long if they try!

Pollution, pollution.
You can use the latest toothpaste,
And then rinse your mouth with industrial waste.

Just go out for a breath of air,
And you'll be ready for Medicare.
The city streets are really quite a thrill,
If the hoods don't get them, the monoxide will.

Pollution, pollution.
Wear a gas mask and a veil;
Then you can breathe,
Long as you don't inhale.

Lots of things there that you can drink
But stay away from the kitchen sink.
The breakfast garbage that you threw into the Bay
They drink at lunch in San José.

So go to the city.
See the crazy people there.
Like lambs to the slaughter
They're drinking the water —
And breathing the air!

WHERE HAVE ALL THE FLOWERS GONE?

Pete Seeger

Where have all the flowers gone,
Long time passing?
Where have all the flowers gone,
Long time ago?
Where have all the flowers gone?
The girls have picked them ev'ry one.
Oh, when will you ever learn?
Oh, when will you ever learn?

Where have all the young girls gone,
Long time passing?
Where have all the young girls gone,
Long time ago?
Where have all the young girls gone?
They've taken husbands everyone.
Oh, when will you ever learn?
Oh, when will you ever learn?

Where have all the young men gone,
Long time passing?
Where have all the young men gone,
Long time ago?
Where have all the young men gone?
They're all in uniform,
Oh, when will we ever learn?
Oh, when will we ever learn?

JOE SOUTH

SO THE SEEDS ARE GROWING

Joe South

So the seeds that you once planted now
are growing.
And you're not so sure you like the fruit you taste.
Well, it's never too late to change,
And there's a whole world to rearrange.
But I don't believe we have much time to waste.
I have heard you crying out for freedom,
but the world won't hear.
It keeps rollin' on,
Making you a slave to everything you fear.
Too many voices, not enough ears;
Too little love, too many fears;
Leaving you with chains around your choice.
Someone else is speaking with your voice.
I have seen you spend a lifetime saving for a
rainy day,
And when it gets here you just sit and cry
and wonder why it is that way.
Well, there are freer people locked up in a prison.
Freedom starts, baby, when your mind has risen
Above the things that bind you to the earth,
And past the ones computing what you're worth.

JOAN BAEZ

WHAT HAVE THEY DONE TO THE RAIN?

Malvina Reynolds

Just a little rain falling all around,
The grass lifts its head to the heavenly sound,
Just a little rain, just a little rain,
What have they done to the rain?

Just a little boy standing in the rain,
The gentle rain that falls for years.
And the grass is gone, the boy disappears,
And rain keeps falling like helpless tears.
And what have they done to the rain?

Just a little breeze out of the sky,
The leaves pat their hands as the breeze blows by,
Just a little breeze with some smoke in its eye,
What have they done to the rain?

Just a little boy standing in the rain,
The gentle rain that falls for years.
And the grass is gone, the boy disappears,
And rain keeps falling like helpless tears.
And what have they done to the rain?

GRASS ROOTS

WALKING THROUGH THE COUNTRY

Dennis Provisor

Off with your shoes, forget those blues;
You're walking through the country.
It's gotta be a groove, with love you'll move,
Walking through the country.
Beautiful sounds blowin' through the trees,
Each a different tune; they're all telling me
You're walking through the country,
Walking through the country,
Walking through the country.

I know there's someone, someone who needs you.
Walk through the country together
And love's gonna come to you.
Groovy day, a sunny day,
Walking through the country.
Just a breeze, and I feel at ease
Walking through the country.
Blades of grass playing with my feet,
And there's nothin' so sweet as the way you
treat me,
Walking through the country.
Walking through the country,
Walking through the country,
Groovy day, a sunny day,
Walking through the country.

WHERE DO THE CHILDREN PLAY?

Cat Stevens

Well I think it's fine building jumbo planes
I'm taking a ride on a cosmic train, switch on
summer from a slot machine, just get what you
want to, if you want, 'cause you can get anything.
I know we've come a long way, we're changing day to
day,
but tell me, where do the children play?
Well you roll on roads over fresh green grass,
for your lorry loads pumping petrol gas, and you
make them long and you make them turn, but they
just go on and on, and it seems that you can't
get off. I know we've come a long way,
we're changing day to day, but tell me where
do the children play?
Well you've cracked the sky, scrapers fill the air,
Well you keep on building high or till there's
no more room up there. Will you make us laugh,
will you make us cry, will you tell us when to live,
will you tell us when to die? I know we've come a long
way, we're changing day to day. But tell me,
where do the children play?

TURN BACK, O MAN

Louis Bourgeois and Clifford Bax

Turn back, O man, forswear thy foolish ways.
Old now is earth, and none may count her days.
Yet thou, her child, whose head is crowned with
flame,
Still wilt not hear thine inner God proclaim,
"Turn back, O man, forswear thy foolish ways."

Earth might be fair and all men glad and wise.
Age after age their tragic empires rise;
Built while they dream, and in dreaming weep:
Would man but wake from out his haunted sleep,
Earth might be fair, and all men glad and wise.

Earth shall be fair, and all her people one.
Nor till that hour shall God's whole will be done.
Now, even now, once more from earth to sky
Peals forth in joy man's old undaunted cry,
"Earth shall be fair, and all her folk be one!"